25

WHY THIS IS AN EASY READER

- This story has been carefully written to keep the young reader's interest high.

- It is told in a simple, open style, with a strong rhythm that adds enjoyment both to reading aloud and silent reading.

- There is a very high percentage of words repeated. It is this skillful repetition which helps the child to read independently. Seeing words again and again, he "practices" the vocabulary he knows, and learns with ease the words that are new.

- Only 217 different words have been used, with plurals and root words counted once.

   Nearly one-half of the words in this story have been used at least three times.

   Almost one-fourth of the words in this story have been used at least six times.

   Some words have been used 19, 26, and 31 times.

ABOUT THIS STORY

- The quiet humor of this gentle tale will please the young reader; he will enjoy being smarter than the innocent little animals confronted with the mystery of the green thing. This story lends itself to dramatization, and leads naturally into any unit or activity on animals.

The Big Green Thing

Story *by* MIRIAM SCHLEIN
Pictures *by* ELIZABETH DAUBER
Editorial Consultant: LILIAN MOORE

WONDER BOOKS

1107 Broadway, New York 10, New York

Introduction

These books are meant to help the young reader discover what a delightful experience reading can be. The stories are such fun that they urge the child to try his new reading skills. They are so easy to read that they will encourage and strengthen him as a reader.

The adult will notice that the sentences aren't too long, the words aren't too hard, and the skillful repetition is like a helping hand. What the child will feel is: "This is a good story—and I can read it myself!"

For some children, the best way to meet these stories may be to hear them read aloud at first. Others, who are better prepared to read on their own, may need a little help in the beginning—help that is best given freely. Youngsters who have more experience in reading alone—whether in first or second or third grade—will have the immediate joy of reading "all by myself."

These books have been planned to help all young readers grow—in their pleasure in books and in their power to read them.

Lilian Moore
Specialist in Reading
Formerly of Division of Instructional Research,
New York City Board of Education

Something was in the sky.

The kitten saw it.

She was sitting in the sun.

She looked up and saw

a green thing, up in the sky.

7

It was coming down—

right out of the sky!

It was getting bigger and bigger!

The kitten ran.

She ran as fast as she could,

to hide behind a tree.

8

The big green thing came down
on the grass.
The kitten peeked out
from behind the tree.
But the big green thing
did not run after her.
It just lay there on the grass.

The kitten came out
from behind the tree.
She took one step,

two steps,

three steps.

"What is it?"

thought the kitten.

"It came out of the sky.

Is it a bird?

I will ask a bird."

11

The kitten ran across the grass

till she saw a little bird.

She called to the bird,

"Please come with me.

I want to show you something."

The kitten and the bird

went to look at the big green thing.

There it lay on the grass.

It did not move.

"What is this?"

asked the kitten.

"Is it a bird?

It came out of the sky

like a bird."

The little bird took one step,

two steps,

three steps.

She looked at the big green thing.

"It has a tail,"
said the bird.
"But it has no feathers.
No. It is not a bird."

She looked again.

"Let's see if it will eat,"

said the bird.

They put an apple and some cookies

in front of the big green thing.

But it still did not move.

It just lay there on the grass.

"It still does not move,"
said the kitten.
"Maybe it is sick."

"Let's leave it here to rest,"
said the bird.

"I have a friend in the woods.

He knows so many things.

Let's ask him what to do."

And off they went to the woods.

"Here is my friend,"
said the bird.

The friend was a rabbit.
The kitten and the bird
told him about the thing
that came down from the sky.

"It can fly,"
said the bird.
"But it is not a bird."

"It has a tail,"
said the kitten.
"But it is not a kitten."

"Does it have big ears?"
asked the rabbit.

"No ears," said the kitten.

"Please come and look at it,"
said the bird.

The rabbit hopped off

with the kitten and the bird.

Then he stopped.

"Does it have big teeth?"

he asked.

"No teeth," said the kitten.

23

So the rabbit went along

to see the big green thing.

There it lay on the grass.

The rabbit took one hop,

two hops,

three hops.

"No big teeth?"

he asked again.

"No teeth," the kitten told him.

The rabbit looked again.
There was no fur
on the big green thing.
No feathers. No legs!

"It is not a pony,

a goose,

a dog,

a rooster,

or a duck,"
said the rabbit.

"We know THAT," said the kitten.
"But what IS it?"

27

"Hello, hello!" said the rabbit

to the big green thing.

"It doesn't talk," he said.

"Maybe it is hungry.

Here," he said.

"I have a carrot and an egg."

He put the carrot and the egg
down on the grass.
But the big green thing
still did not move.
Not even a little bit.

29

"Let's ask the bullfrog,"
said the rabbit.
"He lives in the pond.
He knows so many things."

The rabbit hopped up
to the big green thing.
"Don't worry," he said.
"We will be right back."
And they all went to look
for Bullfrog.

They found him in the pond.
They told him about
the big green thing
that came down from the sky.

"No feathers," said the bird.

"No big ears," said the rabbit.

"But it has a tail,"
said the kitten.
"What is it?"

Bullfrog took some time to think.
"Does it swim?" he asked.

"We do not know,"

said the kitten.

"Please come and look."

So the frog went hopping

along with them

to see the big green thing.

35

He looked at it.

He hopped around it
and around it.

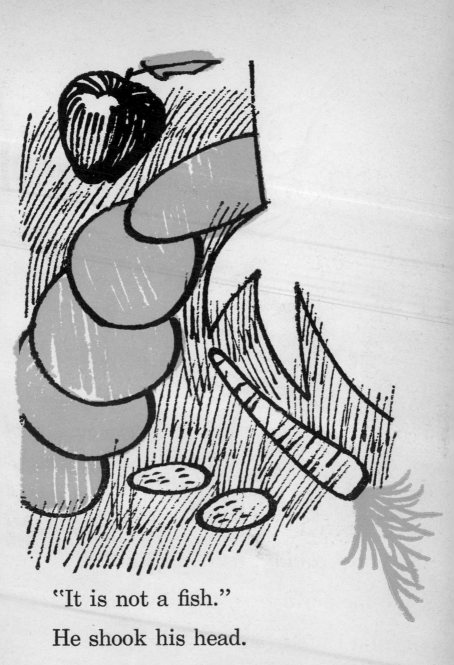

"It is not a fish."

He shook his head.

"It is not a bullfrog," he said.

"How could a fish or a bullfrog
come down from the sky, anyway?"
said the kitten.
"But what is it?"

"I will ask it!" said the rabbit.
He hopped right up
to the big green thing.
"Hello!" said the rabbit.
"Hello, there. Who are you?"

But the big green thing
just lay there on the grass.

"What can we do now?"
said the bullfrog.

"I will ask my boy!"
said the kitten.

"Do you have a boy?"
asked the rabbit.

"Oh, yes. I have a boy
and the boy has me,"
said the kitten.
"Wait here," she said.
"I will get him."
She ran off to find her boy.

He was sitting in front

of his house.

He was rolling up

a big ball of string.

And he did not look very happy.

"Mew!" cried the kitten.

She pulled at his leg.

"Hello, kitty," said the boy.

He went on rolling up

the big ball of string.

"Mew, mew!" cried the kitten
and she pulled at him again.
The boy looked down.
"Do you want me to go
with you?" he said.
"All right. Let's go."

And off they went—the kitten,
with her boy right behind her.
Soon they came to the grass
where the big green thing lay.

45

The rabbit
and the bird
and the bullfrog
were sitting around it.

The boy took one look

at the big green thing.

He picked up his kitten

and gave her a hug.

47

"Kitty," he said,

"you found my new green kite!

I saw it fly away.

I looked and looked for it.

I thought it was lost.

And you found it!"

"A kite!"

The bullfrog looked at the bird.

The bird looked at the rabbit.

The rabbit looked at the kitten.

"A kite!"

Then the boy saw the cookies
and the egg,
and the apple,
and the carrot
lying on the grass,
near the kite.

"Oh, you silly things!" he said.

"Trying to feed a kite!

A kite can't eat.

It's just a toy!"

"Just a toy!"

The bullfrog looked at the rabbit.

"Just a toy!"

The rabbit looked at the bird.

"Just a toy!"

The bird looked at the kitten.

"How silly!" said the bird
to the kitten.
"To ask me about a toy!"

"How silly!" said the rabbit
to the bird.

"Silly!" said the bullfrog.

But what was the boy doing?

He was putting some string

on the big green thing.

Then he began to run with it.

He ran and ran.

And up went the green kite—

up into the blue sky.

"It looks so pretty up there,"
said the kitten.

"No feathers," said the bird.

"No big ears," said the rabbit.

"Silly!" said the bullfrog.

"Anyone can see it's a kite!"

Then the boy ran back

to the kitten and her friends.

"Thank you," said the boy.

"I thank all of you

for finding my kite.

Come on," he said.

"Now let's have a picnic."

And that's what they did.

They all sat down.

They ate the apple,

the carrot,

the cookies,

and the egg,

right then and there.

And they all became good friends.

All because of the green kite!

CHOOSE FROM THESE EASY READERS